Classics In
Child Development

Classics In
Child Development

Advisory Editors

JUDITH KRIEGER GARDNER
HOWARD GARDNER

Editorial Board

INTRODUCTION TO THE
TECHNIC OF CHILD ANALYSIS

By
ANNA FREUD

ARNO PRESS
A New York Times Company
New York — 1975

Reprint Edition 1975 by Arno Press Inc.

Reprinted from a copy in
  The Clark University Library

Classics in Child Development
ISBN for complete set: 0-405-06450-0
See last pages of this volume for titles.

Manufactured in the United States of America

—————◆—————

Library of Congress Cataloging in Publication Data

Freud, Anna, 1895-
    Introduction to the technic of child analysis.

    (Classics in child development)
    Translation of Einführung in die Technik der Kinder-
analyse.
    Reprint of the 1928 ed. published by Nervous and
Mental Disease Pub. Co., New York, which was issued as
no. 48 of Nervous and mental disease monograph series.
    Includes index.
    1. Child analysis. I. Title. II. Series.
III. Series: Nervous and mental disease monographs ;
no. 48.
RJ504.2.F7313 1975 618.9'28'917   74-21408
ISBN 0-405-06460-8

Nervous and Mental Disease Monograph Series No. 48

INTRODUCTION TO THE
TECHNIC OF CHILD ANALYSIS

By

ANNA FREUD

OF VIENNA

AUTHORIZED TRANSLATION SUPERVISED BY

L. Pierce Clark, M.D.

OF NEW YORK

NERVOUS AND MENTAL DISEASE PUBLISHING CO.
New York and Washington
1928

PREFACE

This little monograph, the first of its kind in any language, is a series of lectures to psychoanalysts. It calls attention to the necessity of understanding the child-nature and the peculiar type of transference by which the child may be analyzed. In the actual analyses which Miss Freud gives us, we as well as she are disappointed to find that the old proven and specific methods of adult analysis are not applicable to the child. Those who cannot improvise on the old technic had best leave this new field alone, for the present at least.

Inasmuch as child analysis gives all possible clues to the content of the infantile neurosis, it furnishes direct confirmation of that which we have derived heretofore only inferentially from adult analysis. But we are finally reminded that the infantile neurosis is fashioned from the same psychic structures—instinctive life, ego and super-ego—as in the adult. The importance of recognizing that the external world projects far into the child's internal relation is brought out convincingly. The author tentatively recommends a sharing instead of an entire assumption of the parental transference.

Miss Freud excellently summarizes the difficulty in this new field of applied psychoanalysis by her statement that the practical analysts will say that what she has accomplished with children is a " wild " method which borrows from psychoanalysis without proving just to strictly analytic prescriptions. However, if an adult should apply for psychoanalytic treatment and should prove so impulsive, so undeveloped, and so dependent on his environment as the child patient, one would probably agree with her that the Freudian analysis is an excellent method but is not adapted to such individuals, hence it could not injure the analytic method if one should seek to apply it in modified fashion, particularly if the analyst recognizes fully just what he is doing.

Many of us have already found the work of so much value in the psychoanalytic approach to children that I have been glad to offer this translation to the American psychoanalysts who may not have read the book in the original. Miss Freud is to be congratulated for this unique effort.

L. PIERCE CLARK

The Psychoanalytic Institute,
Stamford, Conn.
March 15, 1928.

CONTENTS

INTRODUCTION TO THE TECHNIC OF CHILD ANALYSIS

BY

ANNA FREUD *

CHAPTER I

INTRODUCTION TO CHILD ANALYSIS

It is difficult to say anything about child analysis unless a decision has been reached as to what cases it is advisable to treat, and what cases had best not be attempted. Mrs. Melanie Klein of Berlin has, as you know, occupied herself extensively with this question, both in her published works and in her lectures before the last congress. She maintains that every disturbance of the psychic or intellectual development of the child can be removed or at least be favorably influenced through analysis. She goes even further in her opinion that analysis is of great advantage for the development of the normal child and, in the course of time, will become an indispensable adjunct to all modern education. On the other hand, it appears, from a discussion of this question at one of the meetings of our society last year, that the majority of our Vienna analysts hold a different view and maintain that an analysis of a child is opportune only when a real infantile neurosis is actually present. In the course of my lectures I fear I can do little toward clarifying this issue. At best I can only report to you in what instances I have undertaken analysis where this decision has proven to be correct, and where its fulfilment

---

Four lectures delivered at the School of Instruction of the Vienna Psychoanalytic Society.

* Authorized translation supervised by L. Pierce Clark, of "Einführung in die Technik der Kinderanalyse," Internationaler Psychoanalytischer Verlag. First published in Archives of Psychoanalysis, July, 1927.

has miscarried because of internal or external difficulties. Of course it is natural that in making new decisions one is guided by successes and deterred by failures.

On the whole, I believe that in working with children, one sometimes gains the impression that analysis is a method too difficult, expensive and complicated for them; that it is used too much, and still more frequently, in other cases, that straight analysis accomplishes too little. From this, it might follow that analysis, when it has to do with children, requires certain modifications and alterations or it can be applied only under definite precautions. Where there is no possibility of keeping these technical precautions, it is perhaps better to advise against the analysis.

In the course of these lectures, numerous examples will illustrate what the preceding remarks refer to. For the time being I will intentionally put aside the solution of these questions and occupy myself with the technical procedure of child analysis in cases in which it appears advisable to undertake analysis for some reason which need not be explained for the moment.

During the past year I have been invited several times to present the development of a child case before the technical seminar of the society and by means of it to explain the special technic of child analysis. Until now I have always refused this request because I feared that all that can be said on this theme would seem to you extremely commonplace and self-evident. The special technic of child analysis, so far as it can be termed special, may be deduced from a simple premise: that the adult—at least in the majority of cases—is a mature and independent being, the child, an immature and dependent one. Obviously enough when the object is so different, the method cannot remain the same. Many parts of it, which in the case of the adult are important and meaningful, lose their significance in the new situation, the rôle of the various methods is shifted; what was in one instance a necessary and harmless action becomes in the other a doubtful procedure. These modifications, however, arise naturally from the actual situation and scarcely need a special theoretic explanation.

During the past two and a half years I have had the opportunity to conduct protracted analyses of some ten children and in the following lectures I will endeavor to correlate the observations I was able to make and which, no doubt, would have occurred to any one of you under similar favorable circumstances.

We will, therefore, keep to the actual succession of events in the analyses and begin with the attitude of the child at the beginning of analytic work.

Let us first consider the analogous situation in the adult patient. An individual feels disturbed by some sort of internal difficulty which interferes with his work or his enjoyment of life; for some reason he gains confidence in the therapeutic powers of analysis or in some particular analyst and determines to seek relief in this way. Naturally I know that the situation is not always like this. Not always internal difficulties motivate the analysis but more frequently conflicts with the outside world, which arise from them. Moreover, the decision is not always arrived at independently; the insistence of relatives or other intimates plays a greater rôle than is often favorable for later work. Even confidence in analysis or the analyst is not always important. At the same time, in the interest of the treatment it remains an ideal and desirable situation if the patient of his own free will allies himself with the analyst against a fragment of his own soul life.

With the child, this state of affairs is naturally never found. The decision to be analyzed never proceeds from the little patient but always from the parents or from others in his environment. The child is not asked for his consent. Even if the question should be put to him, he would have no possible way of forming an opinion or finding an answer. The analyst is a stranger; the analysis itself something unknown. But, what carries even more weight: the ailment in many cases is not the concern of the child; he himself often feels nothing of the trouble; only his environment suffers under his symptoms or his outbursts of temper. Thus everything is lacking in the situation of the child, which seems indispensable to that of the adult: insight into the illness, the voluntary decision and the will to be cured.

But this does not impress every analyst as a serious obstacle. For example, you learned from the work of Mrs. Melanie Klein how she meets these circumstances and what technic she has founded upon them. For my part, it seems worth the effort to investigate whether the situation which has proven so favorable for adult analysis cannot be produced in the case of the child; that is, whether all the readiness and willingness, which are here lacking, cannot be engendered in some way.

As the subject of my first lecture, I will take six cases with ages ranging from the sixth to the eleventh year in order to show you how I succeeded in making the young patient " analyzable " in the adult sense, that is, producing in him an insight into his illness, arousing confidence in the analysis and the analyst, and transforming the decision to be analyzed from an outward one to an inner one. Given this task, it is necessary to have a period of preparation in child analysis, which we do not find in adult analysis. I wish to emphasize that all that is undertaken during this period has nothing to do with the actual analytic work; that means, there is as yet no question of revealing unconscious processes or of influencing the patient analytically. It is merely a matter of converting a definite undesirable condition into a desirable one by all the means which are at the disposal of the adult in his relation with the child. This period of preparation—the " training " for analysis as one might term it—will last the longer the further the original condition of the child is removed from that just depicted for the ideal adult patient.

You must not, however, envisage this work as so difficult; the step, which must be taken, is often not a very great one. I am reminded here of the case of a little six-year-old girl, who was placed in my care for three weeks' observation. I was to determine whether the difficult, taciturn and unpleasant nature of the child was the fault of a defective constitution and unsatisfactory intellectual development or whether the case was that of a particularly inhibited and dreamy child. Closer observation revealed the presence of a compulsion neurosis unusually severe and deep-seated for this age side by side with the keenest intelligence and sharpest logic. Here the whole beginning turned out to be very simple. The little girl already knew two children who were being analyzed by me, and, the first time—she came to the session with her somewhat older girl friend—I did not speak in particular to her but merely allowed her to become acquainted with the strange surroundings. The next time, when I had her alone, I began the first attack. I said that she must know why her two companions came to me; one because he could never tell the truth and wanted to break himself of the habit; the other, because she cried too much and was herself angry over this. Had she been sent to me for some such reason? To this she replied frankly: "I have a devil in me. Can it be taken out?" For the moment, I was amazed at this unexpected answer. Then I replied I thought it could be done, but that it was no easy task and, if I should try to remove it for her, she would have to do a number of things, which would be very unpleasant for her. Naturally, I meant by this that she would have to tell me everything. She paused a moment meditating earnestly. "If you tell me," she answered then, "that this is the only way to do it and to do it quickly, then it will be all right with me." By this she had, of her own free will, pledged herself to the basic analytic principle. More we do not require even of the adult at the beginning. But she also had a complete understanding of the question of how much time would be involved. After the three probational weeks had elapsed, the parents were undecided as to whether to allow her to remain in analysis with me or whether to have her treated in some other manner. She herself, however, was very disturbed, did not wish to give up the hope of recovery, which I had awakened in her, and continued to demand urgently that if she had to go away that I free her from her devil in the three or four days that remained. I assured her that would be impossible, for she would have to remain with me a long time. I could not make her understand anything in numbers, for, although she was of school age she had no knowledge of calculation, because of her numerous inhibitions. Whereupon she sat down on the floor and pointed to the patterns in my carpet. " Will it take as many days," she asked, " as there are red spots here? Or still as many more as these green spots here? " I indicated by means of the many small medallions in the pattern of my carpet the great number of hours that were necessary. She understood perfectly and in the controversy that now followed she did her part to persuade her parents of the necessity of a long joint labor with me.

You will say that in this case it was the severity of the neurosis which facilitated the work of the analyst. But I believe that would be a mistake. As example, I will cite another case, where the initiation took place in a like manner, although in this case there could be no question of an actual neurosis.

About two and a half years ago, I made the analytic acquaintance of a girl almost eleven years old, whose upbringing caused her parents the greatest difficulties. She belonged to the well-to-do middle class, but her home environment was not satisfactory, her father weak and uninterested in her, her mother dead for some years, her relations with the second wife of her father and with her younger stepbrother disturbed by all sorts of troubles. A number of the child's thefts, and an endless series of crude lies, as well as concealments and deceptions big and little, had determined the stepmother, on advice of the family physician, to seek the aid of analysis. Here the analytic agreement was just as simple. " The parents can do nothing with you " was the foundation of our compact. " With their help alone, you will never get away from these constant scenes and conflicts. Perhaps you will try once with a stranger." Without more ado, she accepted me as an ally against the parents, just as the little compulsive neurotic previously described has accepted me as an ally against her devil. The insight into the illness which the compulsive neurotic had, was here replaced by an insight into the conflict, but the active factor common to both was the amount of suffering, originating in the latter case from external, in the former from internal causes.

My method of action in this second case was exactly that of Aichhorn's in his dealings with the delinquent pupils from the public institutions. The state educator, says Aichhorn, must first of all ally himself with his delinquent wards and assume that they are right in their attitude toward their environment. Only in this way will he succeed in working with his pupil instead of against him. I would like to emphasize here that Aichhorn's position in this kind of work has advantages over that of the analyst. He is empowered by the city or the state to interfere and has the authority of his office to back him. On the other hand, the analyst, as the child knows, has been commissioned and is paid by the parents, and he is put in a difficult position, if he turns against those who have put him in charge, even in their own interest. As a matter of fact I never sat opposite the parents of this child in all of our necessary conferences without a bad conscience, and after several weeks, in spite of the best internal conditions, the analysis finally broke up over external matters on account of this unexplainable attitude.

In both of the cases at least the necessary preliminaries to the beginning of actual analysis were easily created; the sense of suffering, the confidence and the desire to analyze. Let us now jump to the other extreme, a case in which not one of these factors was present.

This is the case of a ten-year-old boy with an obscure mixture of many phobias, nervosities, deceptions and childishly perverse actions. One large and several petty thefts had occurred in the preceding years. The conflict with parental authority was not obvious nor conscious, nor on the surface was there any insight into the whole unsatisfactory condition or a wish to change matters. His attitude toward me was completely antagonistic and mistrustful, and his efforts were directed entirely toward protecting his sexual secrets from discovery. Here I could make use of neither of the two methods, which had shown themselves to be so practicable in the other two cases. I could not ally myself with his conscious ego against a split-off fragment of his personality, for he was not even aware of such a splitting, nor could I offer myself as ally against the outside environment, to which, so far as he was aware, he was united by very strong feelings. The method I had to pursue here was obviously another, more difficult and less direct one. I had to inveigle myself into a confidence, which could not be won directly, and to force myself upon a person who was of the opinion that he could get along very well without me.

I now attempted this in several ways. First, for a long time I did nothing but adapt myself to his caprices and follow his moods through all paths and bypaths. If he came to the session in a cheerful frame of mind, I, too, was gay; if he was serious or depressed, I acted in the same manner. If he chose to spend the session under the table instead of moving about, sitting or lying down, I acted as if this were the most natural thing in the world, lifted the tablecloth and talked to him below. If he came with string in his pocket and began to exhibit odd knots and tricks with it, I showed him that I was able to make still more curious knots and to do more remarkable tricks. If he made faces, I could make still better ones, and if he challenged me to tests of strength, I showed him that I was unsurpassably the stronger. Moreover, I fell in with him even in conversation on every subject, from tales of pirates and geographical information to stamp collections and love stories. In these conversations no theme was too grown up or too questionable, and his suspicion could not once detect any educational intent behind my communications. I acted much as if I were a movie film or a paper back novel, which has no other object than to attract the spectator or reader, and which, for this purpose, reduces its interests and aims to those of its public. My first intention was actually nothing more than to make myself interesting to the youngster. That at the same time in this first period I learned a great deal about his superficial interests and inclinations was an unreckoned but most welcome additional gain.

After a while I allowed a second factor to enter in. In a harmless way I proved useful to him during the session, wrote letters for him on the typewriter, was ready to help him in writing down his day dreams and his original stories of which he was very proud, and, during the hour, even manufactured all sorts of little things for him. In the case of a little girl, who was going through the same period of preparation, during the sessions I crocheted and knitted industriously and gradually clothed all her dolls and Teddy bears. Thus, one might say, I developed a second agreeable characteristic: I was not only interesting but I was also useful. As an additional gain of this second period, I was gradually introduced by means of writing letters and stories into the boy's circle of acquaintances and his phantasy activity.

Then something happened which was of even greater importance. I allowed him to observe that being analyzed had great practical advantages, for example, punishable acts had a much different and more favorable ending if first the analyst and through him the edu- cator heard of them. Thus he accustomed himself to use the analysis as a protection against punishment and to seek my assistance in making good thoughtless acts, allowed me to restore pilfered money to its place, and transferred to me all unpleasant but necessary confessions, which were formerly made to his parents. Again and again, on innumerable occasions, he tested my abilities in this respect, before he decided to believe in them. Thereafter there was no more doubt: to him I had become, in addition to being an interesting and useful companion, a very powerful person without whose support he could no longer manage. Thus in these three capacities I had made myself indispensable to him, or, as we might say, he had entered upon a complete relationship of dependence and of transference. I had been waiting only for this moment, in order to demand of him—not by means of words nor at one stroke—very extensive returns, namely, the surrender of his previously hoarded secrets, so necessary for the analysis, which now occupied the next weeks and months and with which the actual analysis began.

You see that in this case I did not trouble to produce an insight into the illness, which came about of itself in the course of the analysis in quite a different fashion. Here the task was merely the creation of an attachment, which would be strong enough to carry the later analysis.

After this detailed description, I fear you will have gained the impression that child analysis depends upon nothing else but this attachment. I should like to try to efface this impression by means of other examples, which hold the mean between the extremes quoted.

I was requested to analyze another ten-year-old boy who had developed symptoms most unpleasant and disturbing to his environment, namely, outbursts of noisy rage and temper, which occurred without any explainable, external occasion, and which were the more striking in an otherwise inhibited and timid child. In this case, it was easy to gain his confidence, for I was already acquainted with him personally. Also the decision to be analyzed was quite in accord with his own wishes, for his younger sister was already my patient and jealousy over the advantages, which she obviously gained from it for her position in the family, forced his inclinations in the same direction. In spite of all this, I could find no point of attack for an analysis. But the explanation of this was not far to seek. He had indeed a certain insight into his phobias and a certain striving to be free of them and of his inhibitions, but the reverse was true of his chief symptom, the outbreaks of rage. Of these he was unmistakably proud and regarded them as something which distinguished him from others, even if not in a very favorable sense, and thoroughly enjoyed them because of the worry he caused his parents thereby. In a certain sense, he felt in harmony with this symptom, and at this time would have probably fought for it, if an attempt had been made to take it from him by analytic means. Here, too, I seized upon a rather deceptive and not too honest remedy. I determined to estrange him from this fragment of his nature. I allowed him to describe the attacks as often as they occurred and appeared to be anxious and thoughtful. I inquired if he were at all master of his actions under such circumstances, and compared his rages to those of a maniac, to whom my efforts to help could be of little use. Thereupon he became puzzled and apprehensive, for to be regarded as crazy was naturally not the goal of his ambition. He now tried of his own accord to control these outbursts; he began to oppose instead of as formerly to support them, and thereby became aware of his actual helplessness in suppressing them, and this realization greatly aggravated his feelings of pain and displeasure. Finally, as I desired, after many vain attempts, the symptom was transferred from a cherished possession into a disturbing foreign body.

It will occur to you that in this instance I produced a condition which was already present in the case of the little compulsive neurotic: a splitting of the inner personality of the child. Also in another case—that of a seven-year-old naughty neurotic girl—after a long preparatory period similar to the one just described, I adopted

the same trick. At one stroke I separated her from the entire per-
sonification of her naughtiness, gave it a name of its own, confronted
her with it, and finally succeeded so well that she began to complain
to me about this newly created person and realized the amount she had
to suffer from it.   Thus the ability of the child to be analyzed goes
hand in hand with producing an insight into the illness.

But even here we must not forget another limitation. For a long
period of analysis I had an unusually gifted and clever girl of eight
years, none other than the previously mentioned oversensitive little
girl who cried too much. She had every intention of changing, had
the ability and the promise to make use of the analysis with me.
But the work with her was always blocked at a certain point and I
was about to content myself with the little I had accomplished—the
disappearance of the most disturbing symptom. Then it became
apparent that an affectionate attachment to a nurse, who was not
friendly to the analysis, was the barrier which our efforts encountered
whenever they began to actually sound the depths. She did indeed
believe what occurred in the analysis and what I told her, but only
up to a certain point which she allowed herself and where her fidelity
to the nurse began.   Whatever went beyond this met with a tenacious
and unassailable resistance. It is true that she repeated in this
manner an old conflict in the love choice between the parents, who
were living apart, and which played a great rôle in the development
of her early childhood. But even this discovery did not help, for
the present attachment to the governess was in every way actual and
habitual. I now began a stubborn and consistent battle with this
nurse for the child's affection, which was waged on both sides with
every weapon, and in which I awakened her critical faculty, sought
to shake her blind dependence and in addition turned to my own
advantage every one of the petty conflicts which occurred daily in the
nursery. I realized that I had won on the day that the little girl
repeated to me one of the domestic incidents which excited her so

much, but this time added to her recital, " Do you believe that she is right? " From then on the analysis began to sound the depths, and of all the cases mentioned it led to the most auspicious success.

The decision as to whether this action, the battle for the child, was permissible, was met without difficulty in this case: the influence of this particular governess would have been unfavorable, not only for the analysis but for the later development of the child. Consider, however, how untenable such a situation becomes if the opponent is no stranger but the parents of the child, or, if the question must be faced, whether it pays in the interest of the success of the analytic work to withdraw the child from the influence of another person which is otherwise favorable and desirable. We will once more come back to this point in detail with the discussion of the question of the practical carrying out of child analysis and its relationship to the environment of the child.

To close this subject, I will add further two short histories which will show you how the child is in a position to grasp the meaning of the analytic effort and the therapeutic task. In this the best was probably accomplished by the little compulsive neurotic girl already mentioned so many times. One day she reported to me an unusually successful struggle with her devil and suddenly demanded my recognition of it. "Anna Freud," she said, " am I not much stronger than my devil? Can't I control him very well alone? I do not really need you at all for this." I wholeheartedly confirmed her in this, that she was much stronger, even without my help. " But I need you anyway," she continued after meditating a moment. " You must help me, so that I will not be so unhappy, when I must be stronger than he is." I believe one could expect no better understanding even in an adult neurotic of the change which is hoped for from the analytic cure.

And now still a second history: My bad ten-year-old, whom I have described in such detail, in a late period of his analysis, got into a conversation in the waiting room with one of the adult patients of my father. The latter told him about a dog who had killed a chicken, and he, the owner of the dog, had had to pay for it. "That dog should be sent to Freud," said my little patient. "He needs analysis." The man did not reply, but later expressed himself disapprovingly. "What kind of an absurd idea had the youngster about analysis? There was nothing the matter with the dog. It wants to kill the chicken and it does so." I knew exactly what the youngster meant by it. He must have thought: "The poor dog; he would so much like to be a good dog and something in him forces him to kill chickens."

You see that here the little neurotic delinquent without difficulty shifts the insight into his naughtiness in place of the insight into his illness, and it becomes for him the complete motive for the analysis.

THE METHODS OF C. ᴅ ANALYSIS

I imagine that my last conclusions have made a strange impression upon the practical analysts among you. All my acts as I have presented them to you contradict in too many points the rules of psychoanalytical technic as they have heretofore been laid down.

Let us once more glance over my different actions: I promise the little girl certain recovery out of consideration that a child cannot be expected to traverse a strange route toward an uncertain goal with a hitherto unknown person. Thus I satisfy her evident desire to be guided by authority and to be cradled in safety. I offer myself openly as an ally and, in common with the child, I criticize the parents. In another case I begin a secret combat against the domestic environment and with all sorts of means strive for the love of the child. I exaggerate the seriousness of a symptom, and frighten the patient in order to attain my end. Finally I insinuate myself into the confidence of the children and thus obtrude myself on human beings who are of the conviction that they can get along very well without me.

What is left of the prescribed tactful reticence of the analyst— the prudence with which he represents to the patient how uncertain is the possibility of recovery or even improvement, the full reserve in all personal matters, the absolute sincerity in the diagnosis of the disease and the full liberty which is given the patient to discontinue treatment of his own volition at any moment? Although the last condition is kept as regards the child patients, it remains more or less a fiction, just as school children are led to believe that they are learning for themselves, to get along in life, and not for the benefit of the

15

teacher or the school. If the freedom which springs therefrom were taken too seriously, the classroom would probably be empty on the following morning. I should defend myself against the assumption which may have arisen in you that I have acted thus in ignorance or unintentional neglect of the rules. In meeting a new situation I think I have only further developed certain attitudes which, without emphasizing it further, you have all adopted toward your patients.

In my first lecture I may have exaggerated the difference between the initial situation of the child and that of the adult. You know how uncertain, in the first days of treatment, the resolve and the confidence of the patient appear. We are in danger of losing him before the analysis is even begun and gain the foundation for our actions toward the patient only when we hold him definitely in the transference. In these first days, however, we set about working upon the patient almost imperceptibly—certainly without any special effort on our part—by means of a series of things which are not so different from my long persisting and deliberate efforts with children.

Let us take for example a depressive, melancholic patient. It is true that the analytic therapy and technic are not exactly suited for these cases. However, when such cases are undertaken a period of preparation is included during which the interest and courage of the patient for analytical work is aroused through sympathy and appreciation of his personal needs. Or let us taken another case. The technical rules do indeed warn us against interpreting dreams too early, thereby revealing to the patient insight into his unconscious processes, for which as yet he can have no understanding but only resistance. With a clever and educated compulsive neurotic who doubts everything, we should be glad to reveal to him right at the beginning of the treatment a particularly beautiful and impressive dream interpretation. Thus we arouse his interest, satisfy his high intellectual demands—and, at bottom, act in nowise different than the child analyst who shows a youngster that he can do better tricks with string than the child himself. For the case when we ally ourselves on the side of the rebellious and neglected child and show that we are ready to help him against his environment, there is also an analogy. We also have to show the adult neurotic that we are there for his help and support and we must take his part exclusively in all conflicts with his family. Here, too, we demonstrate our interest, and make ourselves useful. But the question of power and of outward authority also plays a rôle. Observation shows that the experienced and respected analyst finds it much easier to hold his patients and to protect them against " absconding " in the first stages of analysis than the young beginner; that even in the first sessions the patient establishes far less " negative transference "—expressions of hate and distrust—than toward the former. We may explain this difference from the inexperience of the young analyst, his lack of tact in his attitude toward the patient, and his precipitation or overcaution in his interpretation. I believe that just here is where one must take into consideration the factor of external authority. Not without reason, the patient asks himself who this person really is who lays claim to becoming such a tremendous authority for him and whether his position in the outside world and the attitude of other healthy people toward him justify the claim. One does not necessarily have to deal here with a revival of old hate impulses but rather perhaps with an expression of sound common sense, which arises before the patient permits himself to be carried away by the transference situation. In this estimate of the state of affairs, the eminent analyst of name and reputation plainly enjoys the same advantages as the child analyst, who from the first is bigger and older than his little patient, and becomes a person of undoubted power, when the child feels that this authority is esteemed by the parents as greater than their own.

These could as well be the prerequisites for such a preparatory period of treatment in adult analysis, concerning which I have already

spoken. But I think I have expressed myself incorrectly on th
subject. It would have been more correct to say that in the techni
of adult analysis we still find vestiges of the precautions which hav
proven necessary in dealing with the child. The measure in whic
we use them will probably be determined by the degree in which th
adult patient whom we are treating has remained an immature an
dependent being, thus, in this respect, approximating the child.

So much for the introduction to the treatment: the constructio
of the analytic situation. In what follows let us imagine that th
child has actually gained confidence in the analyst, by means of a
the indicated measures, and possesses insight into his illness, an
now, out of his own resolve, strives to alter his condition. With th
we reach our second theme: a survey of the methods which stan
at our disposal for the actual analytic work with the child.

In the technic of adult analysis we have four such aids. We firs
use everything which the conscious recollection of the patient ca
supply, in order to reconstruct as fully as possible the history of h
illness. We make use of dream interpretation. We digest an
interpret the ideas which the free association of the analyzant pre
sents. And finally, through the interpretation of his reactions to th
transference, we gain access to all of those fragments of his pas
experience which in no other way could be brought into conscious
ness. In the following you must allow me to make a systemati
survey of these methods as regards their application and utilizatio
in child analysis.

In the construction of the history of the patient's illness from hi
conscious recollections, we already encounter the first difference. I
the case of the adult, as you know, we avoid asking for any informa
tion from his family and we depend exclusively on what the patien
himself tells us. The basis of this deliberate restriction is the fac
that communications of relatives are for the most part untrustworth
defective, and colored by their personal attitude toward the sick one

ut the child cannot tell us much about the history of his illness. His memory, before the analyst comes to his aid, does not reach far back. For the time being he is so absorbed by the existing present that by comparison the past fades away. Moreover, he himself does not know when his abnormalities began and when his nature began to differ from that of other children. As yet he has no sense of comparison with others and still fewer self-appointed tasks by means of which he can measure his failures. Hence the child analyst actually obtains the history of the illness from the parents of the little patient. There is nothing left for him to do but to take account of all possible inaccuracies and distortions based on personal motives.

On the other hand, in dream interpretation we have a field in which nothing new is to be learned by the application of adult to child analysis. The child dreams neither more nor less than the adult in analysis; as in everyone, the clarity or incomprehensibility of the dream content depends upon the strength of the resistance. The dreams of children are certainly easier to interpret, even if in the analysis they are not always as simple as the examples given in "The Interpretation of Dreams" (Freud). We find in them all the distortions of wish fulfillment corresponding to the complicated neurotic organization of the child patient. But nothing is easier for the child to comprehend than the interpretation of dreams. When the first dream is related, I say: "The dream cannot do anything alone. Every piece has come from somewhere," and then, in company with the child, I go in search of them. The child amuses himself with the search for individual dream elements as with a Chinese puzzle, following with much satisfaction the individual images or words into the situations of actual life. Perhaps this occurs because the child is nearer to dreams than the adult; perhaps it is only on this account that he is not astonished to find a meaning in the dream because he has never heard the scientific view that dreams are only nonsense. In any case the child is proud of a suc-

cessful dream interpretation. Besides, I have often found that eve
unintelligent children, who were in all respects as unsuitable fo
analysis as possible, do not fail at this point. I have carried out tw
such analyses over a long period almost wholly by means of th
dream.

But even when the associations of the child dreamer are missin
an interpretation is often possible in spite of this. It is so muc
easier to know the situation of the child, to oversee the day's experi
ence, and the number of persons in his environment is so muc
smaller. Often one may venture to insert the missing association
in the interpretation from one's own knowledge of the situation. Th
two following examples of children's dreams, which offer nothin;
new, will merely once more demonstrate the conditions just described

In the fifth month of the analysis of a nine-year-old girl I finall
arrive at a discussion of her masturbation which, only with sever
feelings of guilt, she is induced to confess. During masturbatiol
she had strong passionate feelings and her repulsion against he
activity with her genitals extended to these burning sensations. Sh
began to be afraid of fire and rebelled against wearing warm clothing
She could not watch the flame burning in a gas water-heater, which
adjoined her bedroom, without fear of an explosion. One evening
in the absence of her mother, the nurse wanted to light the bath
heater but not knowing how called on her eldest brother for help.
But he was equally unable to light it. The little girl stood there and
had a feeling that she ought to know how to do it. The following
night she dreamed of the same situation, only in the dream she was
really helping them, did it wrong, and the heater exploded. As punishment, the nurse held her in the fire so that she must burn up.
She awakened in great anxiety, at once aroused her mother, told her
the dream, and added (out of her analytic knowledge) that it was
certainly a punishment dream. She could give no further associations, which in this case, however, I could easily supply. Obviously

playing with the stove stood for playing with her own body, which she also assumed in the case of her brother. The " wrongness " about it was the expression of her own criticism; the explosion probably the form of her orgasm. As a consequence, the nurse, who represents the admonisher against masturbation, carries out the punishment. Two months later she had a second fire dream with the following content: " On the radiator lay two bricks of different color. I know the house is about to burn down and I am afraid. Then someone comes and takes the bricks away." On waking, she finds her hands on her genitals. This time an association helps her out in the dream fragment concerning the bricks: she has been told that if bricks are put on your head you do not grow. From now on the interpretation can be completed without difficulty. Not to grow is one of the punishments she fears for masturbation; the meaning of fire we know from the first dream to be the symbol of her sexual excitement. Of course she masturbated while sleeping, was warned by a recollection of the masturbation prohibition, and suffered fear. The unknown person who removed the bricks was probably myself with my quieting reassurances.

Not all dreams which occur in child analysis interpret themselves with so few difficulties. On the whole, however, the last mentioned little compulsive neurotic was right when she used to announce to me the dream of the preceding night in the following words: " To-day I had a funny dream, but you and I will soon find out what it all means."

Along with the interpretation of dreams, that of the day dream also plays a great rôle in child analysis. Several of the children from whom I was able to gather experience were great day dreamers; the narration of their phantasies became of the greatest aid to me in the analysis. It is usually very easy to induce children, whose confidence has been won in other fields, to tell their day dreams. They discuss them more readily and are obviously less ashamed than the adult, who condemns his fancies as childish.   Whereas the adult, just because of his shame and condemnation, admits his day dreams only late and with hesitation into the analysis, with the child their sudden appearance in the difficult preparatory stage is often very helpful. The following examples produce for you three types of such phantasies.

The simplest type would be the day dream as a reaction following some experience of the day.   For example, the little dreamer just mentioned, at a time when the struggle for supremacy against her brothers and sisters played the leading rôle, reacted against a supposed setback in the analysis with the following dream: " I wish I had never been born.   I want to die.   Sometimes I imagine that I am dead and born again into the world as an animal or a doll.   But if I come back as a doll, then I know to whom I want to belong—to a little girl with whom my nurse used to live and who is very nice and good.   I would like to be her doll and wouldn't object at all if I was treated as dolls are treated.   I would be a charming little baby doll; she could wash me and do everything for me.   The little girl would love me best of all.   Even if she should perhaps again get a new doll for Christmas, I would still be her favorite.   She would never love another doll as much as her baby doll."   It is probably superfluous to add here that two of her brothers and sisters, against whom her jealousy was most strongly directed, were younger than she.   Out of no conversation or association could her momentary situation be more clearly realized than out of this little phantasy.

At the beginning of her analysis, the six-year-old compulsive neurotic was living with a neighboring family.   She had one of her attacks of naughtiness, which was much criticized by the other children.   Her little girl friend even refused to sleep in the room with her, which hurt her feelings very much.   However, in the analysis, she told me that because she was so good the nurse had given her a present of a toy rabbit, and, at the same time, she assured me that the other children liked to sleep with her. Then she related a day dream that had suddenly occurred to her while she was resting. She had not known at all that she was making it: "Once upon a time there was a little rabbit to whom his family were not at all nice. They wanted to send him to the slaughter house and have him killed. But he found it out. He had an old automobile which, however, could still be driven. In the night he fetched it, climbed in, and drove away. He came to a charming little house in which a little girl lived (here she mentioned her own name). She heard him crying downstairs and went down and let him in. Then he stayed and lived there with her." Here there definitely breaks through her feeling of not being wanted, from which she would like to be spared, both in the analysis with me and manifestly before herself. She is twice present in the dream: on one side as the little unloved rabbit, on the other as the girl who is going to treat the rabbit as well as she herself would like to be treated.

A complicated second type is the continued day dream. With children who invent such day dreams or "continued stories" it is often very easy to put yourself enough in touch with them, even in the early period of analysis, so that you may hear daily the newly invented fragment of day dream. From these daily continuations the present inner situation of the child may be constructed.

As a third example I will mention a nine-year-old boy whose day dreams, although made up of people and situations that differed widely, always repeated the same result in innumerable situations. He began the analysis with the narration of an abundance of such fancies which he had stored up in him. In many of them the two principal persons were a king and a hero. The king threatens the hero, wants to torture and to kill him, while the hero escapes in all possible ways. The mechanical innovations, especially an air fleet, play a great rôle in the chase. Of great importance also is a cutting machine, which sends out from both sides when it moves sickle-like knives. The phantasy ended with the victory of the hero, who does everything to the king which the latter wished to do to him.

Another of his day dreams depicts a teacher who punishes and strikes the children. Finally the children surround and overpower her and beat her to death. Still another has to do with a beating machine, in which finally, in place of the prisoner who was to be tortured, the torturer himself is locked. He had stored in his memory a whole collection of such phantasies in endless variations. We divine, without knowing anything more about the boy, that beneath all of these phantasies lies the defense and revenge for a threat of castration; that is, in the day dream, the castration is carried out on the one who originally threatened it. You will concede that, given such an analytic beginning, it is possible to construct an entire series of probable associations for the future course of the analysis.

A further technical aid, which next to the use of dreams and day dreams comes to the fore in many of my child analyses, is drawing, which for the time being in three of my enumerated cases almost replaced all other communications.

Thus the before mentioned girl who dreamed about fire, at the time she was occupied with her castration complex ceaselessly drew a fearful looking human monster with an exaggerated chin, long nose, and endlessly long hair and frightful teeth. The name of this constantly recurring monster was " Biter," his occupation manifestly the biting off of the virile member, which in so many ways he had developed on his own body. A series of other drawings, which during the session she completed either silently or as an accompaniment to her stories, portrayed all sorts of creatures, children, birds, snakes, dolls—all with endlessly long arms, legs, beaks and tails. On another sheet of the same period, quick as a flash she assembled all the things she wished to be: a boy (in order to possess a penis) ; a doll (in order to be the best beloved) ; a dog (which to her was the representative of virility) ; and a sailor, which she took from a phantasy in which she as a boy accompanied her father alone on a trip around the world. Above these figures was added still another drawing from an old fairy tale, which she half remembered and half invented—a witch who was tearing out a giant's hair—hence again a picture of the castration, for which during this time she reproached her mother. Very remarkable was the effect of a series of pictures from a much later period, where, directly in contrast, a queen was presenting a little princess who was standing before her with a wonderful flower with a long stem (obviously again a penis symbol).

The pictures drawn by the little compulsive neurotic were very different. At times she accompanied the narration of her anal phantasies, which filled the first part of her analysis, with illustrations. For example, she drew a picture of an anal " Land of Cockagne " in which, in place of the mounds of porridge and tarts of the tale, the people were obliged to eat their way through enormous piles of excrement arranged in rows. In addition, however, I own a series of the most delicate and colorful pictures of flowers and gardens which she executed with tremendous care, neatness, and charm during the time she was unfolding to me her anal day dreams, which were " stiff with dirt."

But I fear I have sketched for you thus far a too ideal picture of the conditions in child analysis. The family readily supplies all necessary information; the child discloses itself as an eager dream interpreter, who produces an abundant flow of day dreams and, at the same time, furnishes a series of interesting drawings, from which conclusions may be drawn concerning its unconscious impulses. From all these descriptions it would be quite unintelligible why thus far child analysis has always been considered a particularly difficult field for analytic technic, or why so many analysts declare that they can do nothing toward the treatment of children.

The answer is not difficult to find. All of the advantages mentioned are annulled, because the child refuses to associate. The analyst is thus thrown into a dilemma, for the actual means on which the analytic technic is founded can scarcely be brought into practice. To assume the comfortable rest position prescribed for the adult, to eliminate consciously all criticism of the emerging associations, to exclude nothing from the communication, and in this way to skim off the surface of consciousness, manifestly contradicts the nature of the child.

To be sure, a child, with whom one has established a bond in the described manner and to whom one has become indispensable, can be induced to do anything. Thus occasionally, on request, he also associates for a short time and to please the analyst. Such an interjection of associations can indeed be of great usefulness and suddenly clear up a difficult situation. But it will always retain the character of an isolated aid, not the definite basis upon which the whole analytic work can be founded.

Occasionally when I was at a loss how to proceed, I used to ask a little girl, who proved to be especially obedient and compliant to my wishes in the analysis and who along with her great talent for drawing had a decided visual gift, to " see pictures." Thereupon she would sit down in a peculiar squatting position and with closed eyes tensely follow the processes that went on within. Once in this way she actually gave me the solution to a long drawn out resistance situation. The theme at the time was the struggle against masturbation and the separation from her nurse, to whom she had retreated with redoubled affection in order to protect herself against my efforts of liberation. I asked her to " see pictures " and the first picture that emerged brought the answer: " The nurse flies away over the sea." That meant, according to further additional pictures, in which nothing but devils danced about me, that I would force the nurse to go away. Then she would no longer have any protection against her temptation to masturbate and would be made " bad " by me.

More frequently than these willed and requested associations, now and then there come to our aid unexpected and uncalled-for ones. I again take the small compulsive neurotic as an example. At the height of her analysis, the problem was to make plain to her her hatred against her mother, from which knowledge in the past she had protected herself by the creation of her " devil," the impersonal representative of all her hate impulses. Although up to this point she had accompanied me willingly, she now began to resist. But, at the same time, at home she got into all possible kinds of defiant naughtiness, by means of which I daily proved to her that one can only act that way toward a person one hates. Finally under pressure of constant reappearing proofs, she yielded outwardly but now desired to know from me the reason for such feelings of hatred against the mother, whom apparently she loved so much. Here I had to refuse further information, for I was at the end of my knowledge. Then, after a moment of silence she said: " I always believe that a dream, which I once had (several weeks before) and which we have never understood, is to blame." I asked her to repeat it, which she did: "All of my dolls were there and also my rabbit. Then I went away and the rabbit began to cry so terribly. At that moment I felt so sorry for the rabbit. I believe I am now always imitating the rabbit and for that reason cry just as he does." In reality, however, the condition was naturally reversed, the rabbit imitated her, not she the rabbit. In this dream she represents the mother and treats the rabbit as she had been treated by the mother. In this dream association she had at last found the reproach, which her consciousness had refused to make against the mother, that she had always gone away just when the child needed her most.

A few days later she reported the incident for a second time. When after temporary relief, her whole mood was again gloomy, I urged her to contribute still more to the same theme. She knew nothing further but suddenly after deep thought began: " It is so beautiful in G— that I would like to go there once more." Upon closer questioning, it became apparent that in this summer resort she must have spent one of her most unhappy periods. Her older brother, because he had whooping cough, was taken back to his parents in the city and she was isolated with the nurse and two younger children. " The nurse was always angry when I took the toys from the little ones," she said quite spontaneously. Already at that time there existed the supposed preference of the parents for the older brother, and the still more actual one of the nurse for the younger children. On all sides she was neglected and reacted in her own particular manner. Thus again through recollection, this time of the rustic beauty of that place, she was able to find one of her heaviest reproaches against the mother.

I would not emphasize these three cases of astonishing association if similar ones were more common in child analysis. You know that in adults we are not accustomed to anything else.

This lack of voluntary association in the child has caused all who have thus far occupied themselves with child analysis to seek some sort of substitute. Dr. von Hug-Helmuth attempted to replace the knowledge gained from free association of the adult patient by playing with the child, visiting it in its own environment, and seeking to learn all its intimate relations in life. Mrs. Melanie Klein, as her publications describe, replaces the association technic of the adult with a play technic of the child. She starts with the supposition that action is more suitable for the small child than speech. For that reason she places a number of diminutive toys, in short, a miniature world, at his disposal, and thereby creates for him the possibility of acting in this play world. All actions which the child carries out in this way she places on a par with the spoken associations of the adult and accompanies them with interpretations, as we are accustomed to doing with the adult patient. At first glimpse, it would appear that a grievous defect in the technic of child analysis would thus be removed in an unobjectionable manner. However, I would like to reserve for the next lecture an investigation of the theoretic basis of this play technic and to place it in relation to the last point of our consideration, the rôle of transference in child analysis.

CHAPTER III

The Rôle of Transference in Child Analysis

I shall permit myself to again sum up in a few words the contents of my last lecture.

We directed our attention to the methods of child analysis; learned that it is necessary to put together the patient's history from the statements of the family instead of depending upon the patient's information; we discovered the child to be a good dream interpreter and valued the significance of day dreams and free drawing as technical means. On the other hand, to your disappointment I was obliged to inform you that the child is not inclined to engage in free association, and, by this refusal, forces us to seek a substitute to this most important procedure in adult analysis. With the description of one of these substitute methods we finally halted in order to postpone a theoretic appreciation of it until this lecture.

Without doubt the play technic worked out by Mrs. Klein has the greatest value for the observation of the child. Instead of losing time and energy in keeping track of the child in its domestic environment, we transplant at one stroke its entire known world to the room of the analyst, and allow the child to move in it under the eye of the analyst without any interference for the time being. We thus have an opportunity to become familiar with its various reactions, the strength of its aggressive inclinations, its capacity for sympathy, as well as its attitude toward the different objects and persons which are represented by the dolls. As an advantage over an observation of actual conditions, it may be added that this toy environment is manageable and subject to the will of the child, and that it thus may carry out all its actions upon it, which in the actual world, because

30

of its superior magnitude and strength in contrast to the child, remain limited to a phantasy existence. All these advantages make the application of the Klein play method almost indispensable for intimate knowledge of the small child, who is not yet sufficiently capable of expressing itself in words.

Mrs. Klein, however, goes an important step further in the application of this technic. She claims the same position for each of the play associations of the child as for the free association of the adult patient and continually translates the actions which the child produces this way into the corresponding thoughts. That is, she endeavors to discover behind every playful action the symbolic value which lies at its root. If the child overturns a lamp post or any other toy figure, she interprets this behavior in some way as aggressive inclinations directed against the father, and if the child causes a collision of two wagons, as an observation of the sexual union of the parents. Above all, her activity consists of an accompanying translation and interpretation of the child's actions, which—similar to the interpretation of free associations in the adult—again prescribes the direction of further processes in the patient.

Let us once more test the justification of making the child's play activity equivalent to adult association. The associations of the adult are indeed " free," that is, the adult patient has excluded all conscious direction and influence on his thoughts, but, at the same time, he is seeking a definite goal; that is, he who is thus associating is undergoing analysis. But the child has no conception of the end in view. At the outset I explained to you by what means I endeavor also to concentrate the thoughts of the child patient upon the analytic goal. Those children, however, for whom Mrs. Klein has elaborated her play technic, above all, children in the first period of sexual maturity, are too young to be influenced in this fashion. Mrs. Klein feels that one of the advantages of her method is that in using it she is spared the necessity of preparing the child for analysis.

Here we could also make an objection to contradict the correspondence which Melanie Klein proposes. If the play associations of the
child are not dominated by the same end in view as that of the adult,
it is perhaps not right to treat its actions always as such. Instead
of having symbolic meaning, they could occasionally have harmless
explanations. The child who overturns a lamp post could have had
on the day before some kind of experience with such an object.
The collision of the two wagons could perhaps have repeated something seen on the street. And the child who ran toward the visitor
and opened her purse need not, as Mrs. Klein thought, have thereby
expressed symbolically its curiosity as to whether a new little sister
was concealed in the body of the mother, but have associated it with
an experience of the preceding day, in which someone who entered
had brought a small gift in a similar bag. Even in the case of the
adult, we have indeed no right to impute a symbolic sense to every
one of his actions or associations but only to those which originate
under the influence of the analytic situation accepted by him.

But the objection which we in this way proffer against the analytical application of the Klein technic, may possibly be weakened from
another angle. It is indeed true that the child's play activity likewise permits the just mentioned harmless interpretation. Why,
then, does it reproduce out of its experience exactly that scene with
the lamp post or the two wagons? Was it not the symbolic meaning
behind this observation which, in the analytic hour, caused it to be
selected and reproduced ahead of others? It is consequently true,
one might say further, that the child in its actions lacks the definite
goal of the analytic situation which guides the adult. But perhaps
it does not need it at all. The adult must eliminate the guidance of
his thoughts by a conscious effort of will and leave the influencing
of them entirely to the unconscious impulses working within him.
But the child possibly does not need such an arbitrary change of

its situation. Perhaps at all times and in every game, it is wholly in the grip of the unconscious.

You see the question whether the correspondence of the child's play associations to the idea association of the adult can be justified, is not readily decided by means of theoretic arguments or counter arguments. Here it is manifestly dependent upon a reëxamination by means of practical experience.

Let us venture with our criticism to still another point. In addition to the actions which the child performs with the toys that are given him, Mrs. Klein as we know makes use of all the undertakings which the child carries out upon the objects found in her room or upon its own person, for interpretation. Here, too, she strictly follows the example of adult analysis. We feel, therefore, entitled to include in the analysis the entire conduct of the patient, towards us in the session as well as all the trivial conscious and unconscious acts which we observe. We depend here upon the state of the transference in which the patient finds himself and which can give to even otherwise unimportant performances a definite symbolic significance.

The question arises here whether the child really finds itself in the same transference situation as the adult, in what manner and in what forms its transference impulses are expressed and in what way they permit being used for interpretation. With this we arrive at the fourth and most important point of our theme: the rôle of transference as a technical aid in child analysis. The decision of this question will at the time furnish us with new material for disproving or confirming the Klein point of view.

You will recall how in the very first session of the treatment I took great care to produce a strong attachment in the child for me and to bring it into an actual dependent relationship. I would not have followed out this intention with so much energy and so many means if I had considered it possible to carry through the analysis

of a child without such a transference. But the affectionate attachment, the positive transference as the analytical term is, is the pre-
requisite for all subsequent work. In this the child goes even
further than the adult, for it has faith only in the person it loves
and then accomplishes something only out of love for that person.

Child analysis requires much more of this attachment than that
of the adult. In addition to the analytical intention, it carries out
part of an educational one, which we will take up more thoroughly
later. Not only child analysis but the whole success of education
stands and falls every time with the emotional attachment of the
pupil for the educator. Even in the analysis of children, we cannot
say that the production of a transference in itself alone satisfies our
intention, no matter whether it be of a friendly or hostile nature.
We know that with adults we can get along over long periods with
a negative transference, which we make use of for our purpose by
means of consistent interpretation and reference to its origin. But
with the child the negative impulses directed against the analyst—no
matter how revealing they may be in many respects—are above
all unpleasant. As soon as possible we must seek to weaken and
destroy them. The actual productive work will always go hand in
hand with a positive attachment.

The creation of such an affectionate attachment was described in
detail in the introduction to analysis. Its expression in phantasies
and in trivial or important actions differs scarcely at all from the
same processes in the adult patient. We are made to feel the negative
reactions at every point where we wish to help liberate a fragment of
repressed material from the unconscious and thereby draw upon
ourselves the resistance of the ego. At this moment we appear to
the child as the most dangerous and feared tempter and receive all
the expressions of hatred and repulsion with which the child usually
meets its own tabooed instinctive impulses.

In the following I reproduce in detail a phantasy of affectionate transference from the little compulsive neurotic patient mentioned so many times. The immediate occasion was manifestly provoked by me, for I had visited her in her home and remained to be present at her evening bath. The next day she began her session with the words, " You visited me in my bath and next time I will come and visit you in your bath." Some time afterwards she told me the day dream she had thought out in bed before falling asleep, after I had gone away. Her own explanatory marginal notes I add in brackets.

"All the wealthy people did not like you; and your father who was very wealthy also did not like you. [That means I am angry at your father, don't you think so?] And you did not care for any-one and did not give lessons to anyone. And my parents hated me, and Hans and Walter and Annie also hated me and all the people in the world hated us, even the people who did not know us, even the dead. Therefore you only cared for me and I for you, and we always remained together. All the others were very rich but we two were quite poor. We had nothing, not even clothing, for they took everything away from us. Only the sofa remained in the room and we both slept upon it. But we were very happy together. And then we thought we ought to have a baby. Therefore we mixed number one and number two together in order to make a baby. And then we both thought it is not nice to make a baby out of that. So we began to mix flower petals and other things together and from that I got a baby. For the baby was inside of me. It remained inside of me quite a long time. [My mother told me that babies stay inside their mothers a long time.] And then a doctor came and took it out. But I wasn't sick at all. [Usually the mothers are sick, my mother says.] The baby was very sweet and adorable and that made us think we, too, would like to be as adorable and we changed ourselves so that we were very little. I was so big (t), and you were so big (T). [I believe that comes from finding out that I would like to be as little as Walter and Annie.]   And because we had nothing at all, we began to build a house, made all of rose leaves and beds of rose leaves and pillows and mattresses all out of rose leaves sewn together.   Where little holes remained, we filled them up with something white.   Instead of wallpaper we had the thinnest glass and the walls were carved in different patterns. Even the chairs were of glass, but we were so light that we were not too heavy for them.   [I think my mother does not figure at all because yesterday I was angry at her.] "   There follows still another detailed description of the furniture and all the things that were made for the house.   Evidently she continued to elaborate the day dream in this direction until she fell asleep.   In it she laid special stress on the fact that in the end our original poverty was completely compensated for and that we then had much prettier things than the rich people first mentioned.

The same patient, however, at other times relates how she is warned from within against me.   A voice says within her, " Do not believe Anna Freud.   She lies.   She won't help you, and will only make you worse.   She will also change your face so that you will be uglier.   All she says is not true.   Be tired now, lie quietly in bed and don't go to her to-day."   But she always orders this voice to be still and says to it, that all of this must first be told in the next session.

Another little patient pictures me, at a time we are discussing her masturbation, in all possible degrading figures—as a beggarwoman, as a poor old lady, and once as myself standing in the middle of my room with nothing but devils wildly dancing about me.

Thus you see, as in the case of the adult, we become the target at which, according to the circumstances, the friendly or the hostile impulses of the patient are directed.   After these examples we would say that the child makes a good transference.   Nevertheless, it is just in this field that another disappointing surprise awaits us: the child does indeed entertain the liveliest relationship with the analyst and, through it, expresses a number of reactions which it has acquired in its relationship to its own parents; and by the fluctuation, the intensity, and the expression of its feelings it gives important hints as to the formation of its character; but it does not form a transference neurosis.

You all know what I mean by this. The adult neurotic in the course of the analytic treatment gradually transforms the very symptoms for which he has undertaken the treatment. He gives up the old objects on which his fancies have hitherto been fixed and centers his neurosis anew on the person of the analyst. We say that he replaces his previous symptoms by transference symptoms, converts his previous neurosis, what ever kind it may have been, into a transference neurosis and now acts out in relation to the person of the new transference, the analyst, all his abnormal reactions. Upon this new foundation, in which the analyst feels himself at home, and on which he can, in common with the patient, investigate the development and the growth of the individual symptoms, upon this field cleared for operation takes place the decisive battle, the gradual insight into the illness, and the uncovering of the unconscious content.

We can suggest two theoretic reasons why this result cannot be directly produced in the little child. One is to be sought for in the structure of the child itself, the other in the child analyst. The child, unlike the adult, is not ready to undertake a new edition of its love relationships, because, as one might say, the old edition is not yet out of print. Its original objects, the parents, are actually in existence as love objects not in phantasy as with the adult neurotic; between them and the child exist all the relationships of everyday existence; all gratifications and disappointments in regard to them are experienced as more than real. The analyst enters the situation as a new person, he will probably have to share with the parents the love or the hate of the child. There exists no need for the child to immediately exchange the parents for him; in contrast to the original objects, he does not offer all the advantages which the adult finds when his phantasy objects may be exchanged for a real person.

Let us fall back upon the Klein method. Mrs. Klein thinks that when the child is hostile to her in the first sessions, repulses her or even begins to strike her, one may see therein a proof of the ambivalent attitude of the child toward the mother. The hostile components of this ambivalence are simply shifted to the analyst. But I believe the facts of the case are very different. The more affectionately the child is bound to the mother, the fewer friendly impulses it has toward strange people. We see this most clearly in the infant, who demonstrates only fear and dislike for everyone except the mother and the nurse. It is indeed even the reverse. Especially with children who are used to very little affectionate treatment at home and have not been accustomed to expressing or receiving any marked tenderness, a positive relationship is produced by the easiest means. Thus they finally obtain from the analyst that which from the first they have expected from the original love objects.

But, on the other hand, the child analyst is little adapted to be the object of a good interpretable transference. In adult analysis we know what attitude to assume for this purpose. We remain impersonal, shadowy, white paper upon which the patient can register all of his transference phantasies, much in the manner of the cinema, where a picture is thrown upon an empty screen. We avoid making prohibitions or granting gratifications. If, in spite of this, we appear to the patient as prohibitive or acquiescent, it is easy to make clear to him that he has taken the material from his own past.

The child analyst, however, has to be anything but a shadow. We have already heard that to the child he is an interesting person, endowed with all impressive and attractive qualities. The educational tasks which, as you will hear, are bound up with the analysis, result in the child knowing exactly what appears to the analyst desirable or undesirable, of what he approves and disapproves. But, unfortunately, such a clearly outlined and in many respects novel personality is a bad object for transference; that means it is of little use when it comes to the interpretation of the transference. To continue the former comparison, the difficulty arising here is the same as if we found a painting already upon the canvas upon which we are about to project a picture. The more elaborate and beautiful in color it is, the more it will contribute to efface the lines of the superimposed picture.

For these reasons the child forms no transference neurosis. In spite of all affectionate and hostile impulses toward the analyst, it continues to act out its abnormal reactions, where they were formerly acted out: in the domestic environment. On account of this, there arises the weighty technical demand in child analysis, that instead of limiting itself to analytical explanation of what occurs in associations or actions under the eye of the analyst, it must direct its attention to where the neurotic reactions are to be found: in other words, to the home of the child. Thus we arrive at innumerable practical and technical difficulties in child analysis, which I only wish to lay before you here without going into actual detail. If we remain at this point, we are obliged to resort to a continual information service concerning the child; we must know the persons of his environment, and to some extent we must be certain about their reactions toward the child. To illustrate with the ideal case, we share the work with actual educators of the child; thus, it is fitting, as has been explained before, that we share with them the love or the hate of the child.

Where the external conditions or the personalities of the parents do not permit such a mutual action to take place, then we are made to feel the end result in the form of a loss of material in the analysis. I recall instances of child analyses which for these reasons I carried on almost exclusively by means of dreams and reveries. Nothing happened in the transference that could be interpreted and of the neurotic material that appeared in the symptoms I lost more than I cared to lose.

Now even at this point—to compare the situation of the child with that of the adult, which is so much better suited to the carrying out of the analysis—there are ways and means, as in the introductory situation of the analysis, to force the child into a transference neurosis. That may become necessary where a severe neurotic illness must be dealt with in an environment which is either antagonistic to the analysis or to the child. In this case it will be essential to separate the child from the family and to place it in some kind of suitable institution. As there are no such institutions at the present time, we have full liberty to imagine one, such as an establishment presided over by a child analyst or—less fantastic—a school controlled by analytical principles and devoted to mutual work with the analyst. In both cases the first result would be a period free from symptoms, during which the child adapts itself to a new, favorable and, for the present, indifferent milieu. The better it feels in this period, the more unsuited and unwilling we will find it for analysis. At this juncture, it would be perhaps best to leave the child severely alone. It will become analyzable again only after it has adapted itself, that is, when it has formed an attachment to the new surroundings under the influence of everyday life, whereby the original objects gradually disappear and when it again revives its symptoms in this new environment and groups its abnormal reactions around new persons—in short, when it has formed a transference neurosis. In an institution of the first type, which a child analyst would preside over,—as yet we are not even able to judge whether such a form would be desirable—we should then have to do with an actual transference neurosis in the adult sense, centered about the person of the analyst as its object. In the other case, we would merely improve the domestic environment artificially, thus creating a substitute home, such as we deem necessary for analytical work and which would allow us to peek inside and whose reactions toward the child we can control and regulate.

Hence the removal of the child from the parental home seems to us technically the most practical solution. But when we speak of the termination of the analysis, you will see how many considerations mitigate against it. By this action we forestall the natural development at a crucial point; we force the premature detachment of the child from the parental objects at a time when it is not capable of independence in its emotional life nor, as a result of external circumstances, has it at its disposal any freedom in the choice of new love objects. Even if we require very long periods of time for the analysis of a child, in most cases there still remains a gap between its termination and the development of puberty during which period the child needs education, guidance and protection in every sense. But who can give us any assurance that after the breaking off of the transference has succeeded, the child will find its way alone to the right objects? It thus returns to the parental home at a time when it has become a stranger there; its further guidance is now, perhaps, confided to individuals from whom we have previously detached it with effort and force. For internal reasons it is not yet capable of independence. Thus we place it in a new and difficult position, in which, moreover, it again finds most of the conditions of the original conflict. Now it can once more travel the old way of the neurosis or, if this route is barred by a successful analytical cure, it can take the opposite course of open rebellion. From the viewpoint of the illness, this may seem an advantage; from the viewpoint of the social order, which in the end counts most with the child, it is no such thing.

CHAPTER IV

The Relation of Child Analysis to Education

You have thus far accompanied me two steps of the way into child analysis. In the last lecture of the course I will ask you to take the third and perhaps most important step of all.

Allow me first to once more make a résumé. As you perhaps will recall, the first section was occupied with the introduction to the treatment of children. We may say that, viewed from the standpoint of analytical theory, its content is completely neutral. I did not describe to you all these petty, childish, and child-like occupations—crocheting, knitting, playing—all the different varieties of courtship in such detail because I consider them so important for analysis, but, on the contrary, in order to show you what a stubborn object the child is, how it refuses to conform to even the most approved methods of a scientific therapy and throughout demands that one meet it in accordance with its own child-like peculiar nature. Whatever we begin with a child, whether we teach it arithmetic or geography, whether we wish to educate or analyze it, we must first of all every time produce a very definite emotional relationship between us and the child. The harder the work we have before us, the greater must be the carrying capacity of this attachment. The introduction to the treatment, that is, the production of this attachment, follows its own rules, which are determined by the nature of the child and which, for the time being, are independent of analytic theory and technic.

The second part of my subject dealt with the actual analysis, whereby I endeavored to give you a survey of the paths by which one can approach the unconscious of the child. As I could not help but notice, this was disappointing to you, inasmuch as it demonstrated that just the very best and most specific methods of adult analysis are inapplicable for the treatment of the child. Thus we must cast aside many of the requirements of science and obtain the material from wherever we can get it. This is not so very different from what usually happens in everyday life, if we wish to get to know an individual in his most intimate existence. Your disappointment is due, I think, to still another consideration. Ever since I have occupied myself with child analysis, I have repeatedly been asked by analyst colleagues if I have not had the opportunity to approach the developmental processes of the first two years of life, upon which our efforts at analytic discovery are ever more and more urgently directed, in quite a different fashion than is possible in adult analysis. The child, they assume, is still so much nearer to that important period that all repressions must be that much less sharply defined and the material that overlays these strata must be that much easier to penetrate. Thus, perhaps undreamed of possibilities are offered for investigation. Up to the present I have always been obliged to answer this question in the negative. As you perhaps noted from the small examples cited, the material which the child furnishes us is indeed clear and unequivocal. It gives us all possible clues as to the contents of the infantile neurosis, the presentation of which I will reserve for another time. It supplies us with many welcome confirmations of facts which up to the present moment we have only been able to maintain by reference to adult analysis. But as far as my previous experiences reach with the technic here described, it does not lead us beyond the boundary where the child becomes capable of speech; in short, that time from whence on its thinking becomes analogous to ours. To me this restriction does not seem difficult to understand theoretically. What we learn in the analysis of adults concerning this remote period is brought to light just by means of free association and the interpretation of transference reactions, hence with the aid of the two means which fail us in child analysis. In addition, our situation here may be compared to that of the ethnologist, who would vainly attempt a shorter cut to prehistoric life from the study of a primitive people than can be had from that of a cultured race.   On the contrary, he would miss among the primitive people all those aids of myth and legend formation from which in a cultured race he could draw conclusions about the historic early periods.   Hence in the small child we miss the reaction formations and cover memories which are first formed in the course of the latency period and from which later the analysis can obtain the material condensed in them.   Instead, then, of being superior to adult analysis, also at this point in the output of material from the unconscious child analysis stands far behind.

And now as to the third and last section of these lectures: the application of the analytic material which we have unearthed after so much arduous preparation on all the paths and bypaths here described. From my previous explanations you will be prepared to hear from me much that is surprising and that deviates from the classic rules.

Let us first consider again in some detail the corresponding situation of the adult.   His neurosis, as we know, is completely an inner concern.   It takes place between three factors: his instinctive unconscious, his ego, and his super-ego, which last represents the ethical and esthetic demands of society.   It is the task of analysis to elevate to another level the conflict between these powers by bringing the unconscious into consciousness.   Up to the present the instinctive impulses have been withdrawn from the influence of the super-ego through a condition of repression.   Analysis frees them and makes them accessible to the influence of the super-ego, by which their further destiny will now be determined.   There now appears in place of the repression conscious criticism, the rejection of one portion while the rest can in part be sublimated and diverted from their sexual goal and in part be permitted to find gratification.   This new favorable outcome is due to the circumstance that the ego of the patient has gone through its whole ethical and intellectual development from the time when it brought about the original repressions up to the time when the analysis carries out its work of liberation; so that now it is in a position to make its decisions in another way than was formerly possible. The instinctive life must now put up with various restrictions and the super-ego must give up many of its exaggerated claims. On the common foundation of conscious activity there comes about a synthesis between the two.

Let us compare this with conditions present in the child patient. The neurosis of the child is just as much an inner concern and is also determined by the same powers, the instinctive life, the ego and the super-ego. But in two respects we are already prepared to find that with the child the external world projects far into its internal relations—a factor which is analytically disturbing but organically important. In the discussion of the introductory situation of child analysis, we were obliged to ascribe such an important point as insight into the illness not to the child but above all to the environment. And in the description of the transference situation, it became apparent that the analyst is forced to share with the child's former objects the impulses of love and hate which it has at its command. We are therefore not surprised that the external world reaches further into the mechanism of the infantile neurosis and the analysis than is the case with the adult.

We stated above that the super-ego of the adult has become the representative of the moral requirements of the community which surrounds the individual. We know that it owes its origin to the identification with the first and most important love objects, the parents, to whom again society transfers the task of carrying out its current ethical demands toward the child and of enforcing the instinct restrictions which social custom demands. Thus, that which originally was a personal demand, proceeding from the parents, becomes, in the course of development from object love of the parents to the identification with them, an ideal ego, which is independent of the external world and its prototypes.

In the child, however, there can as yet be no question of such independence. The separation from the loved first objects still lies in the future; the identifications are only completed slowly and piecewise. A super-ego is indeed present and already at this early period many of the relations between it and the ego appear analogous to those of later mature life. The constant reciprocal relations between this super-ego and the objects to which it owes its origin are not to be overlooked: we could compare them to those existing between two intercommunicating vessels. If the good relations to the parental objects in the external world rise to the surface, there arises with it the authority of the super-ego and the energy with which it puts through its claims. If these relations are made worse, the super-ego is weakened.

Let us take the youngest child as the first example. If, after the first year of its life, the mother or nurse succeeds in accustoming the young child to the control of its excretory processes, we soon obtain the impression that the child fulfils this requirement of cleanliness not only for the adult—that is, out of a desire to please or out of fear of the nurse—but because it has gained a relationship to it, so that it enjoys its cleanliness or is vexed if, in this regard, an accident happens. But we notice again and again that an ensuing separation from the person from whom this cleanliness has been learned—such as a temporary absence of the mother or a change in the nurse— calls into question the new acquisition. The child again becomes as dirty as before its education in cleanliness and reacquires the control which it once had only if the mother returns or if a bond is formed with the new nurse. Nevertheless, the impression that the child has already set itself the task of cleanliness is no complete disappointment. The demand is present but it is only of value to the child if the person responsible for its establishment remains intact as an object in the external world. Where it loses the relation to the object, it also loses the pleasure it had in fulfilling the requirement.

Even at the beginning of the latency period the conditions are as yet no different. Many times in the analyses of adults we can find confirmed how dangerous for the morale and character formation is any disturbance in the attachment of the child to its parents. If, at this time, it loses its parents through any sort of separation, or if they are depreciated as objects—perhaps lowered in its estimation by some mental disease or criminal action, it is in danger of both losing and depreciating its super-ego, many parts of which are already formed, so that it can now no longer oppose to the instinctive impulses which urge for gratification any efficacious inner power. The origin of many anti-socialities and character abnormalities may possibly be explained from this.

To characterize these conditions even at the close of the latency period, I will cite an instance from the analysis of a boy in the pre-adolescent stage. Once at the beginning of the treatment for some reason I asked whether he had any thoughts which one would prefer not to think. He replied: " Yes, when one wishes to steal some-thing." I asked him for a description of such an occasion. He said: " If, for example, I am alone at home and there is fruit on the table, but my parents have gone out and not given me any. Then I can't help but think how I would like to take some. But then I think of something else because I do not want to steal." I asked him if he were always stronger than such thoughts. He affirmed this, saying he had never thus far stolen. Then I asked, " But if your thoughts become too strong for you, what do you do then? " " Still I do not take anything," he added triumphantly, " for then I am afraid of my father." You see his super-ego had arrived at a far-reaching independence, which is expressed in his own desire not to pass for a thief. Where the temptation becomes too great, he must call for support upon the person who is responsible for the presence of this demand, that is, the father and the warnings and threats of punishment which come from him. Another child would, perhaps, in a similar situation have recalled the love of its mother.

To this weakness and dependence of the child ego-ideal-demands, which I maintain here, there belongs still a further observation, which on closer inspection is found to repeat itself at will: the child has a two-fold morality, one for the world of adults and another for itself and its companions of the same age. We know, for example, that the child begins at a certain age to feel shame, that is, he avoids showing himself naked before strange adults, later also before those closely akin to him, and shuns performing his excremental needs before them. But we also know that the same children undress before other children without shame, and it is by no means easy to prevent them from going to the toilet together. Likewise, to our astonishment, we can establish the fact that the child is disgusted with certain things only in the presence of adults, hence, as if under pressure from them; whereas when alone or in company of other children these reactions are absent. I remember a ten-year-old boy who, while out walking with me, suddenly pointed to a heap of cow dung and exclaimed with interest: " Look, what a funny thing that is ! " A moment later he recognized his mistake and blushed. He excused himself to me with the remark that had he at first seen what it was he would not have spoken. But I know that this same boy with his boy associates speaks of excremental processes with pleasure and without shame. The same youngster also assured me on one occasion that when he is alone he can touch his own excrement without feeling any kind of emotion, but when an adult is present it becomes very difficult even to speak of it.

So shame and disgust, these two most important reaction formations which are destined to keep the anal and exhibitionistic strivings of the child from breaking through to gratification, are even after their development still dependent for support and control upon the adult object.

With these remarks on the dependence of the childish super-ego and the two-fold morality of the child in relation to shame and disgust, we have arrived at the most important difference between child analysis and that of the adult. Child analysis is in no wise any longer a private affair which takes place exclusively between two people, the analyst and the patient. In so far as the child super-ego has not yet become the impersonal representative of the requirements taken over from the external world; in so far as it is still organically bound to the external world, will the objects taken from this outer world still play an important rôle in the analysis itself and especially in the last part of it—in the employment of the instinctive impulses liberated from the repression.

Let us once more return to the comparison of the child with the adult neurotic. We have said that in the latter's analysis we have to reckon only with his instinctive life, his ego and his super-ego; we had no need to trouble—if conditions were favorable—with the fate of the impulses which are freed from the unconscious. These came under the influence of the super-ego which bears the responsibility for their further use.

To whom, however, shall we surrender this decision in child analysis? Taking the above into consideration, we must conclude that it should be the educators of the child, to whom its super-ego is still so inseparably bound; thus, in most cases, the parents.

Let us, however, not forget with how much danger this situation is fraught. The same parents or other educators were the ones whose excessive demands have driven the child to an excess of repression and into a neurosis. Here there is not the great interval between the formation of the neurosis and its liberation through analysis, as with the adult patient, who between these two points of time goes through his entire ego development, so that the individual who first made the decision and the one who has gone through this revision can hardly be termed the same person.   The parents who allowed the child to become ill and those who should help it to recover are actually the same people with the same views.   Only in the most favorable cases are they sufficiently enlightened through the child's illness to be ready to mitigate their demands.   Thus it seems dangerous to yield them decision over the fate of the now liberated instinctive life.   The prospects are too great that the child will be obliged to return once more the way of repression and neurosis.   Under such circumstances it would be more economical to spare entirely the tedious and laborious analytical task for liberation.

What may be the alternative?   Would it perchance be permissible to declare the child, by reason of its neurosis and the analysis of it, prematurely of age and to expect of it even the most important decisions as to how it will now proceed with the impulses placed at its disposal?   I do not know on the basis of what ethics and with the aid of what criteria or practical considerations it would be able to seek a way out of these difficulties.   I believe that if the child is left alone and every support withdrawn, it can find only one short and convenient way—that to direct gratification.   We know, however, from analytic theory and practice, that the child in the very interest of preventing neurosis should be held back from experiencing actual gratification at any stage of his necessarily perverse sexuality. Otherwise fixation on the once experienced pleasure becomes a disturbing obstacle for the further normal development and the urge for its revival, a dangerous stimulus for regression at later stages of development.

It seems to me that in this difficult situation there remains but one way out.   The analyst must claim for himself the freedom to direct the child at this important point, in order to insure, to a certain extent, the results of analysis.   Under his influence the child must learn how to behave in respect to its instinctive life.   His point of view will in the end decide what part of the infantile sexual strivings must be repressed or rejected as is applicable to the cultural world and how much or how little can be permitted direct gratification, and what, in the interest of sublimation, must be repressed, for which all aids of education are at his disposal. We can say in short: during the course of the analysis the analyst must succeed in putting himself in place of the ego-ideal of the child and he must not begin his analytical work of liberation before he is certain that he can completely control the child at this point. At this crisis the position of authority becomes important to him, as was already mentioned in the introduction to child analysis. Only when the child feels that the analyst's authority can be placed above that of the parents will it be ready to yield the highest place in its emotional life to this new love object, which ranks along with that of the parents.

If the parents, as stated above, have learned something from the illness of the child, and are inclined to adapt themselves to the analyst's demands, it is possible to have an actual division of the analytic and educational work between the home and the analyst's office, or rather, a coöperation between these two factors. Thus the child's education experiences no interruption even after the completion of the analysis, but goes direct from the hands of the analyst wholly into those of the now more understanding parents.

But if the parents work against the analyst, as the child is bound by its feelings to both, there arises a situation like that in an unfortunate marriage where the child becomes an object of strife. We must not be surprised if there result all kinds of injuries to the character formation such as we know about from the marriage situation. The child plays the father against the mother, the analyst against the parental home, and utilizes the conflict between them in both instances in order to withdraw itself from all demands. This state of affairs will be dangerous if during a resistance situation the child contrives to prejudice the parents against the analyst so that they are induced to break off the analysis. The control of the child is lost at the most unfavorable moment, in resistance and in negative transference, and one can be sure that the child will utilize all of the liberations received from the analysis in an unfavorable way. To-day I would undertake no child analysis where the personality or preliminary analytic training of the parents does not appear to give a guarantee against such a termination.

The necessity of full control of the child by the analyst may be seen in the following example. It has to do with a six-year-old patient, the already mentioned compulsive neurotic. After I had brought her in the analysis to the point of allowing her " devil " to speak, she communicated to me a large number of anal phantasies, at first hesitatingly, then more and more boldly and in detail, as she saw that they elicited no expressions of displeasure on my part. Gradually the session became devoted entirely to anal matters and the office became a place to deposit all of the day dreams which otherwise oppressed her. During these talks with me the oppression, which was constantly present, was removed. She herself designated the time with me as her rest hour. " My hour with you, Anna Freud," she said once, " is my rest hour. There I do not need to hold back the devil. But no," she added, " I have a second rest period : when I am asleep." During the analysis and during sleep she was evidently freed from that which is equivalent in the adult to the constant expenditure of energy in maintaining repression. Her liberation showed itself above all in an altered, attentive and lively nature.

After some time she went a step further. She began to reveal likewise at home some of her previously strictly guarded phantasies and anal ideas. When, for example, certain foods were placed on the table she made a half audible comparison or a " dirty " joke directed to one of the other children. The foster mother of the children then came to me in order to obtain advice. At this time

I did not have as much insight into child analysis as I now possess and took the situation somewhat lightly, giving the admonition that one should neither approve nor disapprove but allow such small defects to pass unheeded. The effect was entirely unforeseen. Under the lack of criticism from without the child lost all moderation, gave utterance to expressions at home which were formerly spoken only in the office and revelled completely as she had done with me alone in her anal ideas, comparisons and expressions. The other members of the family soon felt it to be intolerable and especially because of her behavior at the common midday meal lost all appetite. It came about that first one and then another, children as well as adults, left the table in silence and disapproval. My little patient had behaved like a perverse person or like an adult subject to a psychosis and had thereby placed herself outside of human society. If one failed to punitively remove her from the others the only result was that she was avoided by everyone. At this period every inhibition even in other respects had vanished. She had in a few days been transformed to a bright, arrogant and naughty child who was not entirely displeased with herself.

The foster mother now came to me a second time to complain. The situation was unendurable, she thought, and disturbed the life of the home. What should she do? Could she tell the child that the narration of such things was not so evil in itself, but ask her to refrain from it in her house out of love for her? This I refused. I was forced to realize that I had committed a blunder and had imputed to the super-ego of the child an independent inhibitory strength which it did not possess. As soon as the important people in the outer world had relaxed their demands, the once so severe ego ideal of the child, which had been strong enough to bring forth an entire series of compulsive neurotic symptoms, became compliant. I had relied on this compulsive neurotic rigidity, had been imprudent, and had, as a result, achieved nothing for analysis. For the time being

I had made—one might say—a bad perverse child out of an inhibited compulsive neurotic. But, at the same time, I had spoiled the situation for my work. For this liberated child had her " rest period " now the whole day long, lessened considerably her appreciation of the joint labor with me, and no longer supplied the proper material, for she scattered this throughout the entire day in place of holding it for the session and had lost momentarily the insight into the disease so necessary for the analysis. For child analysis, the maxim that analytic labor can be carried out only in a state of dissatisfaction counts in much greater measure than in adult analysis.

Fortunately the situation presented itself as dangerous only in theory, for in practice it was easy to remove it. I told the foster mother to do nothing at all further and to have some patience. I would again bring the child to order, only could not promise how soon the result would be attained. In the next session with the child I spoke very emphatically and declared that there was a breach of all agreement. I had believed that she would relate to me those filthy things in order to be free of them. Now I saw that this was not at all the case. She would like to say them to every one in order to derive pleasure from it. I had had nothing against it but then I could not perceive why she still needed me. We might as well give up the sessions and let her have her amusement. But if she held to her first intention, then she must tell these things to me alone and no one else; the more she withheld from mentioning them at home, the more they would occur to her in the session and the more I could learn about her and thus free her from them. Now she must decide. She thereupon became very pale and thoughtful, looked at me and said with the same degree of earnest understanding as in the first analytic session, " If you say that is so, then I will say nothing more about it." Whereupon her compulsive neurotic conscientiousness returned. From this day on no word on such subjects crossed her lips at home. She was again transformed back, but she was also changed from a bad and perverse child to an inhibited and disinterested one.

The same transformation I was forced to undertake on several other occasions with the same patient while under my treatment. Invariably after analytic liberation from her unusually severe compulsive neurosis she escaped to the other extreme of naughtiness or perversity. There was nothing left for me to do but to bring about the neurosis myself and to restore once more the " devil " to his rights, each time, naturally, in smaller amounts and greater caution and gentleness than the present educational system would have done it, until finally I brought the child's behavior between the two possible extremes.

I would not have imparted this example to you in such detail were it not for the fact that it illustrates all of the circumstances asserted in this last section on child analysis: the weakness of the child ego-ideal, the dependence of its demands and therefore of its neurosis on the external world, the inability of self-control of the liberated impulse and the resulting necessity for the analyst of having the child in his power in the interests of education.* The analyst therefore combines in his own person two difficult and diametrically contradictory tasks; that is, he must analyze and he must educate, must in one breath permit and forbid, loosen and hold in check again. If he does not succeed in this, the analysis will be a charter for all of the bad habits banned by society. If he does succeed he makes retrogressive a bit of missed education and abnormal development and provides for the child, or for whomsoever decides the fate of the child, the possibility of once more improving its behavior.

---

* This educational authority offers still other advantages to the child analyst. It makes possible the application of the "active therapy" of Ferenczi, a repression of individual symptoms which will then increase the libido stasis and should supply to the analysis more abundant material in this manner.

You know we do not compel any adult patient even at the end of the analysis to become healthy. It is up to him what he will do with this possibility newly offered him, whether he will once more follow the neurosis, whether his ego development permits him to take the opposite course to far-reaching impulse gratification, or whether he will bring about a middle course, the actual synthesis between the two forces present within him. Nor can we force the parents of our little patient to start anything reasonable with the child when it returns to them. Child analysis is no insurance against all the damage which the future can inflict on the child. It works preëminently in the past; thereby indeed it creates a purified and better foundation for the future development.

I believe the conditions already described point to certain important factors. These factors are indicated not only by a definite ailment of the child. Child analysis belongs above all in the analytic milieu, and must provisionally be limited to the children of analysts, of analyzed patients, or parents who contribute to analysis a certain trust and respect. Only here will analytic education during treatment allow itself to be transferred to home education without a break. Where analysis of the child cannot be organically one with other living conditions, but, like a foreign body is injected into other relationships which are thereby disordered, one will probably create for the child more conflicts than treatment in the other direction will be able to dissolve.

I fear that I have again prepared a disappointment in making this assertion to those of you who were already prepared to bring a certain amount of confidence to child analysis.

After I have told you so much about the impossibilities of child analysis, I would like before closing my lectures to speak further of the great possibilities which, despite all its difficulties, seem to me to possess great advantages over adult analysis. There are above all three. We can in the child produce quite other alterations of character than in the adult. The child who through the influence of its neurosis has trodden the path to an abnormal character development need only go a short distance back to enter again the normal road adapted to his real nature. Unlike the adult, he has not yet built up his entire future life, chosen his calling on the strength of his abnormal development, established friendships on this basis, nor any love relations on this foundation which, projected into identifications, influence the development of his ego. In the " character analyses " of the adult we must really shatter his entire life to accomplish the impossible, especially to make actions retrograde and make effects not only conscious but abolish them, if we will really have actual success. Here child analysis has illimitable advantage over adult analysis.

The second possibility concerns influencing the super-ego. The moderation of its rigidity, as you know, is one of the requirements for analyzing the neurosis. But here adult analysis encounters the greatest difficulties and has to battle with the oldest and most important love objects of the individual, the parents, who have introjected themselves through identifications, and, moreover, the remembrance of whom is in most cases protected by piety, which makes it so much more difficult to handle. In children, however, as you have already seen, we have to do with living persons who are actually present in the external world and who are not glorified by memory. If we add to the internal work external effort, and not only attempt to alter through analysis the already present identifications, but at the same time through human endeavor influence the actual objects, the effect will be telling and astonishing.

The same holds true for a third possibility. With the adult we must limit ourselves to aiding him to adapt himself to his environment. It is beyond us and in fact stands wholly outside our intention or the sphere of our power to transform the environment to meet the patient's requirements. But in the case of the child we can do this very thing without great difficulty. The needs of the child are more

simple, easier to satisfy and to supervise; our power combined with
that of the parents, under favorable conditions, easily suffices to pro-
cure for the child at every stage of its treatment and progress exactly,
or as nearly as possible, what he requires.   We thus lighten the labor
of adaptation by trying to adapt the environment to the child.   Here,
too, is a double labor, from within and from without.

I believe, despite all the difficulties enumerated, it is to these three
points we must ascribe the fact that in child analysis we attain alterations, improvements, and recoveries of which in adult analysis we
cannot even allow ourselves to dream.

In closing, I am prepared to hear the practical analysts among you
say, in respect to what pertains here, that what I have accomplished
with children has had, with all of these variations from adult analysis, nothing at all to do with actual psychoanalysis.   It is a " wild "
method which borrows from psychoanalysis but without proving just
in any way to strictly analytic prescriptions.   However, I pray you
to consider the following: If an adult neurotic should come to your
office for treatment, and if on close inspection he should prove to be
so impulsive, so undeveloped intellectually, and dependent to such a
degree on his environment as are my child patients, you would probably say: The Freudian analysis is an excellent method, but it is not
adapted to such people; and your treatment would be a mixed one.
You would give him as much pure analysis as his nature could tolerate
while the rest would be child analysis, because on account of his quite
infantile character he would deserve nothing better.   I think it could
not injure the analytic method if one should seek to apply it in
modified fashion to other objects than strict adherence to a peculiar
and definite object like the adult neurotic.   It cannot be deemed a
reproach if one adapts it for once to a different purpose; but the
analyst should recognize fully just what he is doing.

INDEX

Classics In
Child Development

An Arno Press Collection

Baldwin, James Mark. **Thought and Things.** Four vols. in two. 1906-1915

Blatz, W[illiam] E[met], et al. **Collected Studies on the Dionne Quintuplets.** 1937

Bühler, Charlotte. **The First Year of Life.** 1930

Bühler, Karl. **The Mental Development of the Child.** 1930

Claparède, Ed[ouard]. **Experimental Pedagogy and the Psychology of the Child.** 1911

Factors Determining Intellectual Attainment. 1975

First Notes by Observant Parents. 1975

Freud, Anna. **Introduction to the Technic of Child Analysis.** 1928

Gesell, Arnold, et al. **Biographies of Child Development.** 1939

Goodenough, Florence L. **Measurement of Intelligence By Drawings.** 1926

Griffiths, Ruth. **A Study of Imagination in Early Childhood and Its Function in Mental Development.** 1918

Hall, G. Stanley and Some of His Pupils. **Aspects of Child Life and Education.** 1907

Hartshorne, Hugh and Mark May. **Studies in the Nature of Character. Vol. I: Studies in Deceit; Book One, General Methods and Results.** 1928

Hogan, Louise E. **A Study of a Child.** 1898

Hollingworth, Leta S. **Children Above 180 IQ, Stanford Binet:** Origins and Development. 1942

Kluver, Heinrich. **An Experimental Study of the Eidetic Type.** 1926

Lamson, Mary Swift. **Life and Education of Laura Dewey Bridgman, the Deaf, Dumb and Blind Girl.** 1881

Lewis, M[orris] M[ichael]. **Infant Speech:** A Study of the Beginnings of Language. 1936

McGraw, Myrtle B. **Growth: A Study of Johnny and Jimmy.** 1935

Monographs on Infancy. 1975

O'Shea, M. V., editor. **The Child: His Nature and His Needs.** 1925

Perez, Bernard. **The First Three Years of Childhood.** 1888

Romanes, George John. **Mental Evolution in Man:** Origin of Human Faculty. 1889

Shinn, Milicent Washburn. **The Biography of a Baby.** 1900

Stern, William. **Psychology of Early Childhood Up to the Sixth Year of Age.** 1924

Studies of Play. 1975

Terman, Lewis M. **Genius and Stupidity:** A Study of Some of the Intellectual Processes of Seven "Bright" and Seven "Stupid" Boys. 1906

Terman, Lewis M. **The Measurement of Intelligence.** 1916

Thorndike, Edward Lee. **Notes on Child Study.** 1901

Wilson, Louis N., compiler. **Bibliography of Child Study.** 1898-1912

[Witte, Karl Heinrich Gottfried]. **The Education of Karl Witte,** Or the Training of the Child. 1914